This book belongs to

Game Rules

for couple

Take turns and choose between
TRUTH or **DARE**.

If you don't answer the truth question or complete
your dare, your partner can choose your "punishment".

P.s. You are only allowed 5 truths!

Game Rules

for party with "friends"

Every player sits in a circle, then an empty bottle is placed on a table or on the ground.

- Palyer 1 begins by rotating the bottle.

  The bottleneck now points to player 2.

- Player 2 choose **TRUTH** or **DARE**

  If a dare is chosen, player 2 turns the bottle again to find his/her dare partner!

If player 2 does not answer the truth question or complete his/her dare, player 1 can choose his/her "punishment"!

P.s. Each player are only allowed 5 truths!

#1
TRUTH

What sex act would you never do again?

#1
DARE

Close your eyes, scroll through your contacts list and tell me the sexiest thing about the person you land on.

TRUTH

What's the least amount
of time you've known
someone before you've
had sex with them?

2
DARE

Sing the chorus of a song
you've had sex to.

#3
TRUTH

Who is the most
inappropriate person
you've had a sexual
fantasy about?

#3
DARE

Suck on my finger
and pretend you're
performing oral sex for
30 seconds.

#4
TRUTH

What's a sex act most
people like that you think
is overrated?

4
DARE

Call a local pizza place and try to convince someone that you need a "special" delivery person.

TRUTH

If you had to choose between only oral sex or only penetrative sex for the rest of your life, which one would you pick?

5
DARE

Send a suggestive text
message to someone in
your phone.

6
TRUTH

Is sex better when you're
in love, or better when
the other person is hot
and mysterious?

6
DARE

Put a blindfold on and kiss whatever body part I put in front of your mouth.

#7
TRUTH

What is the largest age gap you've had between you and someone you've had sex with?

#7
DARE

Let me lick your lips and you have to resist kissing or touching me the whole time.

#8
TRUTH

Do you know the last name of everyone you've had sex with?

#8
DARE

Put something edible on my forearm and lick it off.

#9
TRUTH

How many sex partners do you believe is "too many"?

#9
DARE

Go in the bathroom and
take a suggestive selfie
and send it to me.

#10
TRUTH

What's #1 on your sexual
bucket list right now?

10
DARE

Send a Facebook message
to someone you've slept
with describing a dirty
dream you've had about
them.

11
TRUTH

Have you ever taken
someone's virginity?

11
DARE

Call a phone sex line and
pretend that you have a
diaper fetish.

12
TRUTH

Would you rather
dominate someone or be
dominated?

12
DARE

Put a blindfold on and try
to guess which body part
I'm touching you with.

13
TRUTH

What do you think is the sexiest body part of your same sex?

13
DARE

Whisper something in my ear that you think will turn me on.

#14
TRUTH

What's something most people don't like in bed, but you can't get enough of?

#14
DARE

Try to undress me with
one hand.

15
TRUTH

What's the sexiest thing
anyone's ever said to you?

#15
DARE

Try on my underwear.

#16
TRUTH

What's the least sexy thing anyone's ever said to you (while trying to be sexy)?

16
DARE

Use one of your sex toys on yourself for 60 seconds.

17
TRUTH

If you had the power to give or receive unlimited orgasms, what would you pick?

17
DARE

Take off your shirt for
the rest of the game.

#18
TRUTH

What kind of porn did
you last watch?

#18
DARE

Take off your pants for
the rest of the game.

#19
TRUTH

If you had to fuck one animal, what animal would you pick?

#19
DARE

Show me the sexiest
picture you have on your
phone.

#20
TRUTH

How old do you think is "too old" for someone to still be a virgin?

20
DARE

Put whipped cream on a
body part you want me to
lick it off of.

21
TRUTH

If you could have one
sexual superpower, what
would it be?

21
DARE

Fuck me in a room where
we've never had sex
before.

TRUTH

What is a somewhat weird fetish that you would actually try?

22
DARE

Go online and order me a
sex toy you think I'd like.

#23
TRUTH

What fictional character
do you have sexual
fantasies about?

23
DARE

Show me a porn video you'd want us to act out together.

#24
TRUTH

What's the first thing
you'd do if you could
inhabit the body of the
opposite sex for one
hour?

24
DARE

Kiss my neck for 60 seconds.

25
TRUTH

What's the weirdest thing
you've ever done while
masturbating?

25
DARE

Do your best to try to
make me orgasm in the
next 5 minutes.

TRUTH

If you had to choose between having sex with one person for the rest of your life or never being able to have sex with the same person more than once, what would you pick?

26
DARE

Close your eyes and
describe what my body
looks like in detail.

27
TRUTH

Would you rather pay someone to put on a striptease for you (they aren't allowed to touch), pay someone to cuddle and massage you while wearing non-sexy clothes, or pay someone to talk dirty over the phone but never be able to see them?

27
DARE

Try to get me aroused just by touching me, but without touching any sexual parts.

28
TRUTH

What's the least sexual
thing I've done that has
gotten you aroused?

28
DARE

Whisper in my ear
something you've always
wanted to see me do in
bed.

29
TRUTH

If you were forced to
have sex with someone
in your extended family,
who would you pick?

29
DARE

Use your tongue to spell out a secret you have on a part of my body.

TRUTH

What's a common fetish
that you would never try
in real life?

#30
DARE

Kiss my earlobe for 60 seconds.

31
TRUTH

What do you wish
someone would have
told you about sex way
earlier?

31

DARE

Put a blindfold on, stick your tongue out, and try to guess what I touch it with.

#32
TRUTH

Has anyone ever caught you having sex?

#32
DARE

Try to undress me with just your teeth.

33
TRUTH

What non-sexual part of
your body turns you on
the most when I touch it?

33
DARE

Tongue kiss me anywhere
you choose.

#34
TRUTH

What's the biggest lie
you've told in order to get
someone into bed?

#34
DARE

Try not to get turned on while I sit on your lap and kiss your neck for 60 seconds.

TRUTH

Have you ever kicked someone out of your bed immediately after having sex?

#35
DARE

Show me the dirtiest text message you have in your phone.

36
TRUTH

Have you ever had sex
with more than one
person at a time?

36
DARE

Whisper in my ear a sexy
nickname you've never
called me but always
wanted to try.

37
TRUTH

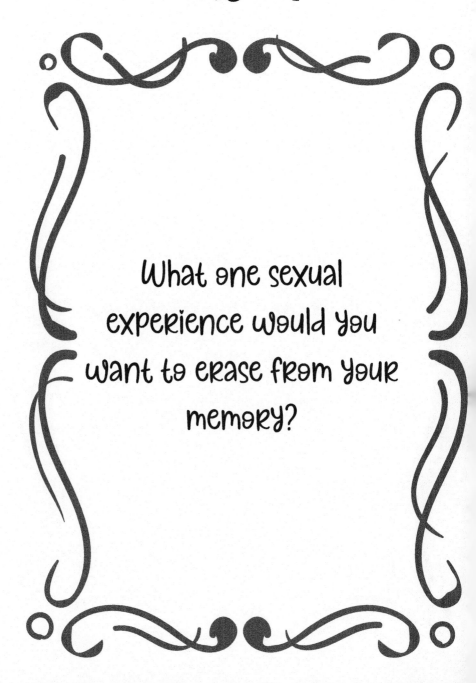

What one sexual experience would you want to erase from your memory?

37

DARE

Go get something from
the fridge and eat it as
seductively as possible.

TRUTH

What one sexual
experience do you think
about most often?

38
DARE

For the rest of the game, pretend you are a cop who wants to arrest me for the crime of being too sexy.

TRUTH

Have you ever called someone (or been called) 'Daddy'?

#39
DARE

Show me with your
hands what you want my
tongue to do.

#40
TRUTH

What's the least amount of time that's passed between you having sex with two different people?

40
DARE

Try to turn me on using touch, but you can only touch my arms and hands.

41
TRUTH

What is your favorite
part of foreplay?

41
DARE

Whisper in my ear
something sexy about
me you've fantasized
about while you've made
yourself cum.

#42
TRUTH

Would you rather fuck
someone 20 years older
or 20 years younger?

42
DARE

Kiss and lick my lips and try to get me to lose control and kiss you.

#43
TRUTH

Would you rather spank someone or be spanked?

43
DARE

Show me the dirtiest image you have on your phone.

#44
TRUTH

If you could double the
amount in your bank
account or double
the amount of sexual
partners you've had,
which would you pick?

#44
DARE

Pick up any book or
magazine in the room
and read from it as
seductively as possible.

45
TRUTH

Would you rather sleep with only insanely hot people or sleep with only people who think you're insanely hot?

#45
DARE

Suck on my toes.

46
TRUTH

How much money would your boss have to offer you before you slept with him or her?

46
DARE

Handcuff me and do
something you've always
wanted to do to my body.

#47
TRUTH

What's the most public
place you'd fuck someone?

47
DARE

Kiss my nipple for 60 seconds.

#48
TRUTH

Do you have any sex tapes?

#48
DARE

Try not to get turned on
while I sit on your lap and
kiss your earlobe for 60
seconds.

49
TRUTH

What's your biggest sexual
fear?

#49
DARE

Blindfold me and kiss your favorite part of my body for 60 seconds.

#50
TRUTH

Would you rather be
spanked or spank me?

#50
DARE

Send me the dirtiest text
you can think of.

Printed in Great Britain
by Amazon